You are beautiful
Eres hermosa

You are smart
Eres inteligente

You are special to me
Eres especial para mi

You are unique
Eres unico

You are not alone
No estas solo

You are cool
Eres genial

You are a good child
Eres un buen niño

You are important
Eres importante

You are loved
Eres amado

You are helpful
Tu eres util

You are enough
Tu eres sulficiente

The Story of
JONAH

written by Dandi

"JONAH!"

Jonah looked around, but saw no one. Then he knew.
The Lord God was calling him!

"Jonah!" God said again. "I want you to go to
Nineveh."

'Nineveh?!' thought Jonah. 'Not there! Anywhere
but there.'

"Jonah, you must warn the people of Nineveh. Tell
them to stop being so bad or something really bad will
happen to them!"

Jonah thought about that, 'Hmmm. I could go to
Nineveh like God says. Or...'

'...On the other hand,' Jonah reasoned, 'what if the people of Nineveh don't want to hear about God? What if they take it out on me? And even if they listen to me and change their ways, what good is that to me? To tell the truth, I'd like to see them get what's coming to them!'

So Jonah made the wrong choice. He decided *not* to obey God. Instead of heading for Nineveh, Jonah set off to the sea in the opposite direction.

Jonah bought himself a ticket on a ship bound for Tarshish. He climbed aboard and watched as the sailors rowed the ship out to sea.

"Ah, this is more like it," Jonah said. "This old ship is the perfect hiding place. Surely God can't find me here. I'll get as far away from Nineveh as I can."

But Jonah was wrong. God blew a strong wind over the sea. The sails of the ship whipped and moaned. The boat creaked as it rocked in the water, tossed by the terrible storm. White-crested waves dashed against the ship. Water splashed over the sides. The sailors struggled as raging waters threatened to pull them all to the bottom of the sea!

Jonah watched in silence as the desperate sailors shouted for help. They threw their baggage overboard to lighten the load and keep them from sinking.

"Do something!" one of the sailors screamed at Jonah. "We don't know who you are or where you come from, but if you have a God, pray! Ask Him to save us! Beg your God for mercy!"

Jonah knew without a doubt that God had sent the storm because of him. God was speaking to him – not with words this time, but with a storm.

"This is all my fault," Jonah admitted. "I worship the God who made the earth and sea. I'm on this ship because I'm running away from God."

"What should we do so your God will stop the storm?" asked the Captain.

"Throw me overboard into the sea!" declared Jonah.

None of the sailors wanted to throw Jonah overboard. They tried harder to row to safety, but nothing helped. Finally, with a prayer to God to forgive them, they did what Jonah asked.

"One, two, three!" They flung Jonah into the sea. And the storm stopped!

'Well, this is the end of me,' thought Jonah as he felt himself fall through the air to the sea below.

Plop! Jonah hit the water. Glub, glub...down he sank!

Just when Jonah could hold his breath no longer, he felt something swim up behind him! Suddenly he heard a GULP! He passed over teeth and tongue inside something very strange – but safe. Jonah realized with a start, he had been swallowed by a huge fish!

It was dark and smelly inside the big fish. For three days Jonah sat and thought, and thought, and thought. Finally, Jonah understood how much trouble he had put himself through by disobeying God – and how much trouble God had gone through to take care of him!

Jonah prayed: "Oh, Lord, I was silly to try to hide from you! You are with me even in the deepest ocean. You sent this huge fish to save me because you love me. I love you too! From now on I'll do whatever you say!"

What happened next made Jonah dizzy with laughter! Round and round the fish swam, with Jonah in his belly. When the fish got close to shore, he opened his huge mouth and spit Jonah right out onto dry land!

"I've got to be on my way," Jonah told the great fish. "You did your job. Now I must do mine!"

This time Jonah took the right road – straight to Nineveh! When he got there, Jonah told the people everything God had said. The people in Nineveh felt sorry for being so mean and bad. They prayed to God and asked for help. They promised to be better and obey Him.

Because of the message Jonah brought to Nineveh, their whole city was saved! From then on, the people of Nineveh worshiped God, who had brought Jonah out of the fish's mouth – to them.

The Story of
JONAH

Look for all the
titles in this series:

The Story of Daniel

The Story of Jesus

The Story of Jonah

The Story of Noah

® Landoll, Inc.
© 1995, Landoll, Inc.
Ashland, Ohio 44805

ISBN 1-56987-367-4   N821
00367

0   87577 00547   8

The Story of NOAH

The Story of
NOAH

written by Dandi

Long, long ago the people of the earth turned their backs on God. They hurt each other so much, it broke God's heart. If God told the people to do one thing, they tried to come up with a plan to do just the opposite. Everybody disobeyed God – except for one man.

Noah loved God with all his heart. Even though everybody around him did mean, rotten things, Noah was kind and good. When God told Noah to do something, Noah did it. That's what made him happy.

Noah did all he could to keep his family according to God's commands. "God always keeps His promises," Noah told his sons, Shem, Ham, and Japheth, time and time again.

One day God spoke to Noah. "Noah, I'm going to cover the earth with water in a worldwide flood. But I'm making you a promise. I'll keep you and your family safe."

Then God told Noah to build a giant boat, an ark, made out of wood. Noah had trouble picturing what an ark would look like because he had never seen one. God gave him all the details. "You'll have to make rooms and stalls; an upper, middle, and lower deck; windows, and a door in the side of the ark."

Noah did everything just as God commanded.

So Noah set about building the ark.

"What are you building, Noah?" asked his neighbors.

"God told me to build an ark," said Noah. "And that's just what I'm doing."

"An ark?" said one bearded man, scoffing. "In the desert? You're crazy!"

"God is sending a flood to cover the whole earth," Noah said, hammering a spike into a board.

"A flood?" Then all the people burst out laughing.

Years went by with no rain. More years passed. People came from miles around to laugh at Noah and his ark. But Noah knew God always keeps His promises. So he did everything God commanded him to.

Finally Noah finished the ark.

God said, "Noah, it's time to gather the animals, a pair of every kind of beast and fish and bird. One week from today, I will bring the rains."

So Noah brought the animals to the ark – a boy and a girl of every kind of creature. Two by two, the animals marched up the ramp and into the ark.

Noah did everything that God commanded him to.

"It's time," Noah told his family. Just as soon as Noah, his wife, his sons and their wives boarded the ark, God slammed the door of the ark shut!

Noah listened. Above the gentle moo of the cows and the quacks of the ducks, Noah thought he heard something. First, a plink, plunk. Then a rat-a-tat. Then a clatter as rain struck the earth with violent force.

For forty days and nights it rained and poured. Noah and his family were safe inside the ark. Noah felt the ark lift higher and higher as the waters rose above the trees, above the mountains.

After forty days, Noah listened, but he no longer heard the pinging on the roof of the ark. The rain had stopped. Five more months the ark floated until it came to rest on top of Mt. Ararat. Months later Noah looked out the window over the vast waters. He could see the tops of the mountains poking through.

"I'll send out a bird," Noah said. He chose a dove, a timid, little bird of peace. "If she finds dry land, she will stay away. Then we will know the earth has dried," he said.

Out flew the little dove. But she found no dry land and returned to the ark. A week later Noah sent the dove again in search of dry land. That night, the dove returned, but this time Noah saw she had something in her mouth. An olive leaf! Noah knew now that the dove had found a tree. The land was becoming dry!

When Noah sent the dove out a week later, he was not surprised that she failed to return. The dove had found dry land and was making her nest in an olive tree!

"It's time to come out, Noah," God told him.

Noah opened the door. Out flew the birds, two by two. Carefully, the animals walked down the ramp in pairs, kicking up their heels when they set foot on dry land.

Last out of the ark came Noah and his family. They praise God for the sunshine on their faces and the dry land and fresh grass at their feet. They thanked God for always keeping His promises.

Then God said, "Look up in the clouds!"

Noah looked up at the most beautiful arc of colors — a rainbow!

"This is a sign of my promise to you," God said. "When it appears in the sky, I will look down on the rainbow and remember my promise to never again flood the whole world."

So when you see a rainbow, remember that God is looking from the other side of that rainbow. It is His promise to you forever.